Thank you...

...for purchasing this copy of Spelling for Literacy for ages 7-8. We hope that you will find these 126 worksheets helpful as part of your programme of literacy activities.

This Spelling for Literacy book is part of our growing range of educational titles. Most of our books are individual workbooks but, due to popular demand, we are now introducing a greater number of photocopiable titles especially for teachers. You may like to look out for:

HOMEWORK TODAY for ages 9-10

HOMEWORK TODAY for ages 10-11

NUMERACY TODAY for ages 5-7

NUMERACY TODAY for ages 7-9

NUMERACY TODAY for ages 9-11

SPELLING FOR LITERACY for ages 5-7

SPELLING FOR LITERACY for ages 8-9

SPELLING FOR LITERACY for ages 9-10

SPELLING FOR LITERACY for ages 10-11

BEST HANDWRITING for ages 7-11

To find details of our other publications, please visit our website: **www.acblack.com**

Andrew Brodie Publications

Suggestions for using this book...

We have examined carefully the current national policies for teaching spelling as part of your literacy work. In writing this book we have included all the spelling patterns and objectives which are specified within these policies. We have arranged the words into sets, usually of sixteen words. Each set of words is used in three styles of sheet:

Sheet A

- ✓ Can be photocopied onto OHP transparencies for discussion.

- ✓ Can be displayed on the wall as 'Words of the Week'.

- ✓ Can be copied onto card and cut up to make matching cards.

Sheet B

- ✓ Activity sheets to be used in the Literacy Hour.

- ✓ Can be hole-punched to go in pupils' personal spelling files.

- ✓ Can be given as homework sheets.

- ✓ **Answers provided on the last three pages of this book.**

Sheet C

- ✓ Has a fold line so that children can copy the words, then cover them to write again without looking.

- ✓ A perfect follow-up activity for the learning which has taken place using sheets A and B.

- ✓ Following the Learn, Write, Check system.

Spelling for Literacy *for ages 7-8*

Contents

Set	Year, Term	Words
Set 1 Sheets A, B & C	Year 3, Term 1 Adding ing	sing, singing, ring, ringing, walk, walking, jump, jumping, paint, painting, dress, dressing, rest, resting, call, calling
Set 2 Sheets A, B & C	Year 3, Term 1 Adding ing	sleep, sleeping, dream, dreaming, feel, feeling, shout, shouting, sail, sailing, boil, boiling, peel, peeling, speak, speaking
Set 3 Sheets A, B & C	Year 3, Term 1 Adding ing, doubling consonant	run, running, hop, hopping, sit, sitting, skip, skipping, step, stepping, grip, gripping, shut, shutting, win, winning
Set 4 Sheets A, B & C	Year 3, Term 1 Adding ing, removing e	hope, hoping, come, coming, smile, smiling, take, taking, care, caring, make, making, divide, dividing, stare, staring
Set 5 Sheets A, B & C	Year 3, Term 1 Words ending in le	paddle, saddle, kettle, nettle, giggle, wiggle, middle, fiddle, muddle, puddle, rattle, cattle, nibble, little, puzzle, nuzzle
Set 6 Sheets A, B & C	Year 3, Term 1 Adding ing to words ending in le	tickle, trickle, pickle, prickle, cackle, crackle, chuckle, chuckling, tickling, trickling, prickling, crackling, tackle, tackling, knuckle, buckle
Set 7 Sheets A, B & C	Year 3, Term 1 able and ible	able, table, cable, vegetable, valuable, reliable, probable, portable, terrible, horrible, visible, invisible, possible, impossible, responsible, sensible
Set 8 Sheets A, B & C	Year 3, Term 1 ble and ple	double, trouble, tumble, stumble, jumble, bumble, grumble, mumble, scramble, thimble, simple, example, sample, crumple, Bible, stable
Set 9 Sheets A, B & C	Year 3, Term 1 dle, gle and cle	candle, handle, bundle, trundle, tingle, single, jingle, jungle, cycle, bicycle, uncle, circle, icicle, miracle, needle, bungle
Set 10 Sheets A, B & C	Year 3, Term 1 Prefix: un	happy, unhappy, tidy, untidy, lucky, unlucky, usual, unusual, zip, unzip, tie, untie, fair, unfair, kind, unkind
Set 11 Sheets A, B & C	Year 3, Term 1 Prefixes: de & dis	code, decode, ice, de-ice, like, dislike, agree, disagree, appear, disappear, connect, disconnect, honest, dishonest, obey, disobey
Set 12 Sheets A, B & C	Year 3, Term 1 Prefixes: re & pre	build, rebuild, visit, revisit, play, replay, write, rewrite, cycle, recycle, place, replace, turn, return, prepare, prefix
Set 13 Sheets A, B & C	Year 3, Term 2 Endings: er & est	fast, slow, faster, slower, fastest, slowest, quick, cold, quicker, colder, quickest, coldest, long, longer, longest
Set 14 Sheets A, B & C	Year 3, Term 2 Adding er & est to words which end in e	late, close, later, closer, latest, closest, wide, safe, wider, safer, widest, safest, nice, nicer, nicest
Set 15 Sheets A, B & C	Year 3, Term 2 Adding er & est to words with short vowels	big, fit, bigger, fitter, biggest, fittest, sad, good, sadder, better, saddest, best, bad, worse, worst
Set 16 Sheets A, B & C	Year 3, Term 2 Adding er & est to words which end in y	happy, foggy, happier, foggier, happiest, foggiest, wavy, funny, wavier, funnier, waviest, funniest, lucky, luckier, luckiest

© Andrew Brodie Publications ✓ www.acblack.com

Set 17 Sheets A, B & C	**Year 3, Term 2** Changing words by adding y	mess, messy, ink, inky, full, fully, fuss, fussy, mood, moody, sleep, sleepy, dream, dreamy, cheek, cheeky
Set 18 Sheets A, B & C	**Year 3, Term 2** Adding y to words with short vowels	fun, funny, run, runny, sun, sunny, tin, tinny, pop, poppy, dot, dotty, rat, ratty, bat, batty
Set 19 Sheets A, B & C	**Year 3, Term 2** Adding y to words ending in e	laze, lazy, ease, easy, smoke, smoky, shine, shiny, rose, rosy, stone, stony, breeze, breezy, bone, bony
Set 20 Sheets A, B & C	**Year 3, Term 2** Adding s to make plurals	boy, boys, girl, girls, table, tables, book, books, desk, desks, time, times, window, windows, house, houses
Set 21 Sheets A, B & C	**Year 3, Term 2** Adding es to make plurals	catch, catches, match, matches, push, pushes, brush, brushes, blush, blushes, fox, foxes, box, boxes, church, churches
Set 22 Sheets A, B & C	**Year 3, Term 2** Making plurals for words with a vowel then y	day, days, key, keys, tray, trays, monkey, monkeys, play, plays, holiday, holidays, birthday, birthdays, buy, buys
Set 23 Sheets A, B & C	**Year 3, Term 2** Making plurals for words with a consonant then y	baby, babies, lady, ladies, puppy, puppies, pony, ponies, party, parties, penny, pennies, hobby, hobbies, fly, flies
Set 24 Sheets A, B & C	**Year 3, Term 2** Strange plurals	man, men, woman, women, child, children, tooth, teeth, mouse, mice, goose, geese, calf, calves, wolf, wolves
Set 25 Sheets A, B & C	**Year 3, Term 2** Silent letters	knee, kneel, knife, knives, know, knock, gnat, gnome, write, wrist, wrap, wrapping, when, where, honest, rhyme
Set 26 Sheets A, B & C	**Year 3, Term 2** More silent letters	comb, bomb, thumb, crumb, lamb, numb, calf, calves, half, halves, calm, palm, could, should, would
Set 27 Sheets A, B & C	**Year 3, Term 2** Compound words	play, playground, motor, motorway, bed, bedroom, every, everybody, everyone, everything, some, somebody, someone, something, somewhere, sometimes
Set 28 Sheets A, B & C	**Year 3, Term 2** More compound words	pan, pancake, week, weekend, goal, goalkeeper, break, breakfast, stairs, upstairs, downstairs, any, anybody, anyone, anything, anywhere
Set 29 Sheets A, B & C	**Year 3, Term 2** Suffixes: ly	love, lovely, nice, nicely, like, likely, safe, safely, real, really, usual, usually, regular, regularly, proper, properly
Set 30 Sheets A, B & C	**Year 3, Term 2** Suffixes: ful	hope, hopeful, care, careful, pain, painful, use, useful, wonder, wonderful, cheer, cheerful, beauty, beautiful, till, until
Set 31 Sheets A, B & C	**Year 3, Term 2** Suffixes: less	hope, hopeless, care, careless, pain, painless, use, useless, home, homeless, speech, speechless, end, endless, harm, harmless
Set 32 Sheets A, B & C	**Year 3, Term 2** Suffixes: er	teach, teacher, farm, farmer, drive, driver, mine, miner, babysit, babysitter, run, runner, shop, shopper, spin, spinner
Set 33 Sheets A, B & C	**Year 3, Term 2** Using apostrophes	is not, isn't, was not, wasn't, did not, didn't, does not, doesn't, will not, won't, cannot, can't, could not, couldn't, should not, shouldn't

© Andrew Brodie Publications ✓ www.acblack.com

Set 34 Sheets A, B & C	Year 3, Term 2 More apostrophes	I would, I'd, I have, I've, they have, they've, she will, she'll, there is, there's, where is, where's, here is, here's, they are, they're
Set 35 Sheets A, B & C	Year 3, Term 3 Prefixes: mis, non, im, ex, in, co, anti	behave, misbehave, sense, nonsense, fiction, non-fiction, stop, non-stop, import, export, interior, exterior, star, co-star, clockwise, anti-clockwise
Set 36 Sheets A, B & C	Year 3, Term 3 Prefixes: bi, re, tri, dis, in, ab, pre, inter, sub	cycle, bicycle, recycle, tricycle, appear, disappear, visible, invisible, normal, abnormal, view, preview, review, interview, marine, submarine
Set 37 Sheets A, B & C	Year 3, Term 3 Days	Monday, Tuesday, Wednesday, Thursday, Friday, Saturday, Sunday, holiday, yesterday, tomorrow, birthday, anniversary, weekday, weekend, fortnight, tonight
Set 38 Sheets A, B & C	Year 3, Term 3 Months and seasons	January, February, March, April, May, June, July, August, September, October, November, December, spring, summer, autumn, winter
Set 39 Sheets A, B & C	Year 3, Term 3 Numbers	eleven, twelve, thirteen, fourteen, fifteen, sixteen, seventeen, eighteen, nineteen, twenty, thirty, forty, fifty, sixty, seventy, eighty
Set 40 Sheets A, B & C	Year 3, Term 3 Numbers and measurements	ninety, hundred, thousand, million, metre, centimetre, millimetre, kilometre, gram, kilogram, litre, millilitre, second, minute, hour, month

Within the National Literacy Strategy, the spelling objectives are heavily weighted towards Term 2, which is quite often the shortest term.

You may wish to work on some of the Term 2 spellings towards the end of Term 1 and at the early part of Term 3.

The three Contents sheets can be photocopied and used as individual or class records, by highlighting words as they are covered or learnt by the children.

● **Adding ing to the ends of words (1).**

sing	singing
ring	ringing
walk	walking
jump	jumping
paint	painting
dress	dressing
rest	resting
call	calling

These words have two consonants at the end.

We don't change them when adding **ing**.

Add **ing** to the words on the left.
The first one is done for you.

sing → singing

ring

walk

jump

paint

dress

rest

call

Two consonants

jump

↓

jumping

Fill in the missing words using some of the **ing** words that you have made.

When I am _____ I put on my socks first.

When we went for a walk, Gina kept _____ up to touch the leaves.

I could hear Tom _____ my name.

I was _____ a picture.

The bells were _____ and I was _____ a song.

Now make up some sentences of your own, using words from the list above.

1. Look carefully
   at each word.

2. Say the word
   out loud.

fold line

3. Copy each word in
   your best handwriting.

4. Look again at the
   first word, then fold
   the paper over it to
   cover it.

5. Write the word in
   COLUMN 3.

6. Check your spelling.

7. Now do the same for
   each word.

Learn, Write, Check.

Name:

Date:

LEARN THE WORD	WRITE THEN COVER	WRITE THEN CHECK
sing		
singing		
ring		
ringing		
walk		
walking		
jump		
jumping		
paint		
painting		
dress		
dressing		
rest		
resting		
call		
calling		

Sheet
A
For use
with OHP,
for display
or
to make
matching
cards.

● **Adding ing to the ends of words (2).**

YEAR
3
Term
1

SET
2
Sheet
A

sleep	sleeping
dream	dreaming
feel	feeling
shout	shouting
sail	sailing
boil	boiling
peel	peeling
speak	speaking

These words have two vowels before the final consonant.

We don't change them when we add ing.

sleep
dream
feel
shout
sail
boil
peel
speak

Add **ing** to the words on the left.
The first one is done for you.

Two vowels

slèèp

⬇

sleeping

sleeping

Fill in the missing words. The first one has been done for you.
Try to find an extra pair of words for each set.

sleep	→	sleeping		sail	→	
sweep	→			nail	→	
	→				→	

eat	→			look	→	
treat	→			cook	→	
	→				→	

Choose four of the **ing** words on this page. Write a sentence for each of these words.

fold line

1. Look carefully at each word.

2. Say the word out loud.

3. Copy each word in your best handwriting.

4. Look again at the first word, then fold the paper over it to cover it.

5. Write the word in COLUMN 3.

6. Check your spelling.

7. Now do the same for each word.

Learn, Write, Check.

YEAR **3** Term **1**

SET **2** Sheet **C**

Name:

Date:

LEARN THE WORD	WRITE THEN COVER	WRITE THEN CHECK
sleep		
sleeping		
dream		
dreaming		
feel		
feeling		
shout		
shouting		
sail		
sailing		
boil		
boiling		
peel		
peeling		
speak		
speaking		

YEAR
3
Term
1

SET
3
Sheet
A

Sheet
A
For use
with OHP,
for display
or
to make
matching
cards.

run	running
hop	hopping
sit	sitting
skip	skipping
step	stepping
grip	gripping
shut	shutting
win	winning

Each of these words ends with a consonant with one vowel in front of it.

If we want to add **ing** we must double the consonant.

Add **ing** to the words on the left.
The first one is done for you.

run → running

A consonant...

shop

...with one vowel in front of it.

Double consonant.

shopping

hop

sit

skip

step

grip

shut

win

Fill in the missing words, using the **ing** words above.

Jasdeep is [   ] with her [   ] rope.

The builder is [   ] the hammer very tightly.

We must go because the shop is [   ].

"Quick, catch the rabbit! He's [   ] away."

Here are some more words which follow the same spelling pattern:

hum   win   spin   swim   stop

In your book, add **ing** to each word - don't forget to double the consonant.
Write a sentence for each word that you have made.

fold line

1. Look carefully at each word.

2. Say the word out loud.

3. Copy each word in your best handwriting.

4. Look again at the first word, then fold the paper over it to cover it.

5. Write the word in COLUMN 3.

6. Check your spelling.

7. Now do the same for each word.

Learn, Write, Check.

Name:

Date:

LEARN THE WORD	WRITE THEN COVER	WRITE THEN CHECK
run		
running		
hop		
hopping		
sit		
sitting		
skip		
skipping		
step		
stepping		
grip		
gripping		
shut		
shutting		
win		
winning		

Sheet
A

For use
with OHP,
for display
or
to make
matching
cards.

● **Removing e to add ing.**

YEAR
3
Term
1

SET
4
Sheet
A

hope	hoping
come	coming
smile	smiling
take	taking
care	caring
make	making
divide	dividing
stare	staring

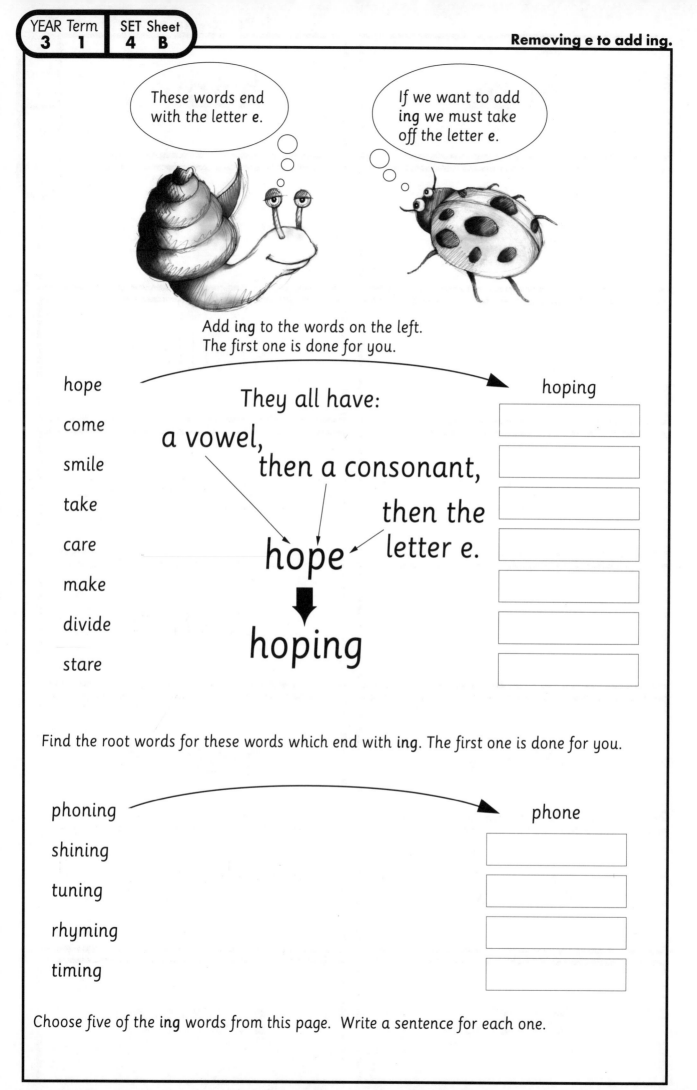

These words end with the letter e.

If we want to add ing we must take off the letter e.

Add **ing** to the words on the left.
The first one is done for you.

hope

come

smile

take

care

make

divide

stare

They all have:

a vowel,

then a consonant,

then the letter e.

hope

↓

hoping

hoping

Find the root words for these words which end with **ing**. The first one is done for you.

phoning → phone

shining

tuning

rhyming

timing

Choose five of the **ing** words from this page. Write a sentence for each one.

Learn, Write, Check.

1. Look carefully at each word.

2. Say the word out loud.

fold line

3. Copy each word in your best handwriting.

4. Look again at the first word, then fold the paper over it to cover it.

5. Write the word in COLUMN 3.

6. Check your spelling.

7. Now do the same for each word.

Name:

Date:

LEARN THE WORD	WRITE THEN COVER	WRITE THEN CHECK
hope		
hoping		
come		
coming		
smile		
smiling		
take		
taking		
care		
caring		
make		
making		
divide		
dividing		
stare		
staring		

Sheet
A
For use
with OHP,
for display
or
to make
matching
cards.

paddle	saddle
kettle	nettle
giggle	wiggle
middle	fiddle
muddle	puddle
rattle	cattle
nibble	little
puzzle	nuzzle

Words which end with le...

...sometimes have double consonants in the middle.

kettle   paddle   giggle
↑   ↑   ↑
double t   double d   double g

Sort the words from the word bank.

WORD BANK

little   dazzle   giggle   nettle   nuzzle   kettle   middle
muddle   saddle   wobble   fiddle   puddle   puzzle
wiggle   paddle   dribble   nibble   rattle   cattle

double z

double g

double d

double b

double t

Can you think of any more words with double letters which end with le?

fold line

1. Look carefully at each word.

2. Say the word out loud.

3. Copy each word in your best handwriting.

4. Look again at the first word, then fold the paper over it to cover it.

5. Write the word in COLUMN 3.

6. Check your spelling.

7. Now do the same for each word.

Learn, Write, Check.

Name:

Date:

LEARN THE WORD	WRITE THEN COVER	WRITE THEN CHECK
paddle		
saddle		
kettle		
nettle		
giggle		
wiggle		
middle		
fiddle		
muddle		
puddle		
rattle		
cattle		
nibble		
little		
puzzle		
nuzzle		

Sheet
A

For use
with OHP,
for display
or
to make
matching
cards.

● Words ending in le, changing to ing.

YEAR
3
Term
1

SET
6
Sheet
A

tickle

trickle

pickle

prickle

cackle

crackle

chuckle

chuckling

tickling

trickling

prickling

crackling

tackle

tackling

knuckle

buckle

Some words which end in le...

...can be changed to end with ing.

Add **ing** to the words on the left.
The first one is done for you.

tickle   tickling

We remove the **e**

tickle

...and put **ing**.

tickling

trickle

pickle

prickle

crackle

tackle

chuckle

buckle

Did you notice that all these words have ck before the ending le?

Choose the correct word to fill each gap:

I like _____ with my cheese.

The water was _____ slowly from the tap.

My friend was _____ about the funny programme on television.

Now choose four words from this page.
Write a sentence for each of your four words.

Learn, Write, Check.

fold line

1. Look carefully at each word.

2. Say the word out loud.

3. Copy each word in your best handwriting.

4. Look again at the first word, then fold the paper over it to cover it.

5. Write the word in COLUMN 3.

6. Check your spelling.

7. Now do the same for each word.

Name:

Date:

LEARN THE WORD	WRITE THEN COVER	WRITE THEN COVER
tickle		
trickle		
pickle		
prickle		
cackle		
crackle		
chuckle		
chuckling		
tickling		
trickling		
prickling		
crackling		
tackle		
tackling		
knuckle		
buckle		

● **Words ending in able and ible.**

able	table
cable	vegetable
valuable	reliable
probable	portable
terrible	horrible
visible	invisible
possible	impossible
responsible	sensible

Some words end in able and some words end in ible.

You need to look at the words very carefully.

WORD BANK

able   horrible   sensible   table   valuable   terrible
cable   vegetable   possible   portable   reliable   invisible
impossible   probable   visible   responsible

Sort the words from the word bank into two lists.

...able words	...ible words

Choose four of these words. Write a sentence for each one.

Some words can have **able** added to them to make new words. Look at these:

admire ➜ admirable

cure ➜ curable

Did you notice that the letter e at the end of **admire** and **cure** had been removed?

In your book, make new words by adding **able** to these words:

love

forgive

believe

move

remove

Learn, Write, Check.

1. Look carefully at each word.

2. Say the word out loud.

fold line

3. Copy each word in your best handwriting.

4. Look again at the first word, then fold the paper over it to cover it.

5. Write the word in COLUMN 3.

6. Check your spelling.

7. Now do the same for each word.

Name:

Date:

LEARN THE WORD	WRITE THEN COVER	WRITE THEN CHECK
able		
table		
cable		
vegetable		
valuable		
reliable		
probable		
portable		
terrible		
horrible		
visible		
invisible		
possible		
impossible		
responsible		
sensible		

Sheet
A
For use
with OHP,
for display
or
to make
matching
cards.

double	trouble
tumble	stumble
jumble	bumble
grumble	mumble
scramble	thimble
simple	example
sample	crumple
Bible	stable

Some of the words in the word bank can be changed to end in ing.

Some <u>cannot</u> be changed to end in ing.

WORD BANK

double   crumple   thimble   fable   scramble   stable
simple   bumble   example   trouble   jumble   sample
mumble   tumble   grumble   stumble

Which of these words cannot be changed to end in **ing**?

Now sort all the words into the sets below.

Words which have letter **u** followed by letter **m**:

Words which have letter **o** followed by letter **u**:

Words which have a letter **m** but <u>not</u> a letter **u**:

Words that end in **ple**?

fold line

1. Look carefully at each word.

2. Say the word out loud.

3. Copy each word in your best handwriting.

4. Look again at the first word, then fold the paper over it to cover it.

5. Write the word in COLUMN 3.

6. Check your spelling.

7. Now do the same for each word.

Learn, Write, Check.

YEAR **3** Term **1**

SET **8** Sheet **C**

Name:

Date:

LEARN THE WORD	WRITE THEN COVER	WRITE THEN CHECK
double		
trouble		
tumble		
stumble		
jumble		
bumble		
grumble		
mumble		
scramble		
thimble		
simple		
example		
sample		
crumple		
Bible		
stable		

● **Words ending in dle, gle or cle.**

Sheet
A
For use
with OHP,
for display
or
to make
matching
cards.

candle	handle
bundle	trundle
tingle	single
jingle	jungle
cycle	bicycle
uncle	circle
icicle	miracle
needle	bungle

Look carefully at the words in the word bank.

Sort them into three sets.

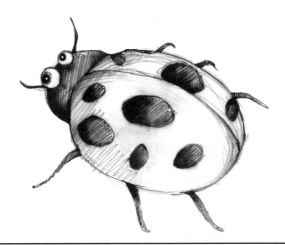

WORD BANK

candle   miracle   bungle   jungle   trundle   cycle   single
uncle   handle   circle   bicycle   jingle   bundle
tingle   needle   icicle

...cle words	...dle words	...gle words

Read this sentence which has lots of **cle**, **dle** and **gle** words:

My uncle and I went into the jungle on our bicycles,
with bundles of food tied to the handlebars.

Try to write your own sentence, using as many of these words as you can.

YEAR
3
Term
1

SET
9
Sheet
C

1. Look carefully at each word.

2. Say the word out loud.

3. Copy each word in your best handwriting.

4. Look again at the first word, then fold the paper over it to cover it.

5. Write the word in COLUMN 3.

6. Check your spelling.

7. Now do the same for each word.

Learn, Write, Check.

Name:

Date:

LEARN THE WORD	WRITE THEN COVER	WRITE THEN CHECK
candle		
handle		
bundle		
trundle		
tingle		
single		
jingle		
jungle		
cycle		
bicycle		
uncle		
circle		
icicle		
miracle		
needle		
bungle		

Sheet
A
For use
with OHP,
for display
or
to make
matching
cards.

● **Using the prefix un.**

happy	unhappy
tidy	untidy
lucky	unlucky
usual	unusual
zip	unzip
tie	untie
fair	unfair
kind	unkind

We can make the opposites of some words...

...just by putting **un** at the start.

happy

Add **un** to the words on the left.
The first one is done for you.

unhappy

tidy

lucky

usual

zip

tie

fair

kind

Fill in the missing words.

I was very [　　　　　] when I got told off.

I had to [　　　　　] my coat because I was so hot.

The hoops were tied together so I had to [　　　　　] them.

You should not be [　　　　　] to other people.

Try to find three other words which can have un added at the start.
Write your pairs of words here:

Learn, Write, Check.

fold line

3. Copy each word in your best handwriting.

4. Look again at the first word, then fold the paper over it to cover it.

1. Look carefully at each word.

2. Say the word out loud.

5. Write the word in COLUMN 3.

6. Check your spelling.

7. Now do the same for each word.

Name:

Date:

LEARN THE WORD	WRITE THEN COVER	WRITE THEN CHECK
happy		
unhappy		
tidy		
untidy		
lucky		
unlucky		
usual		
unusual		
zip		
unzip		
tie		
untie		
fair		
unfair		
kind		
unkind		

● **Using the prefixes de and dis.**

Sheet
A
For use
with OHP,
for display
or
to make
matching
cards.

code	decode
ice	de-ice
like	dislike
agree	disagree
appear	disappear
connect	disconnect
honest	dishonest
obey	disobey

We can make the opposites of some words...

...by using the prefixes **de** or **dis**.

de

code   →   decode

ice   →   de-ice

Notice the use of a hyphen for this one.

dis

like   Add **dis** to the words on the left. The first one is done for you.   dislike

agree

appear

connect

honest

obey

Use the clues to help you to complete this crossword puzzle.

Clues across:
1. not telling the truth
2. We _____ the wires from a battery when we have finished using it.
3. to have a different opinion

Clues down:
4. to solve a message written in code
5. to vanish

Learn, Write, Check.

Name:

Date:

fold line

1. Look carefully at each word.

2. Say the word out loud.

3. Copy each word in your best handwriting.

4. Look again at the first word, then fold the paper over it to cover it.

5. Write the word in COLUMN 3.

6. Check your spelling.

7. Now do the same for each word.

LEARN THE WORD	WRITE THEN COVER	WRITE THEN CHECK
code		
decode		
ice		
de-ice		
like		
dislike		
agree		
disagree		
appear		
disappear		
connect		
disconnect		
honest		
dishonest		
obey		
disobey		

Sheet
A
For use
with OHP,
for display
or
to make
matching
cards.

● **Words which start with pre or re.**

build	rebuild
visit	revisit
play	replay
write	rewrite
cycle	recycle
place	replace
turn	return
prepare	prefix

The prefix re...

...usually means to do something again.

build   Add **re** to the words on the left.   rebuild

The first one is done for you.

visit

play

write

cycle

place

turn

These two words start with **pre**:

prepare   prefix

Can you think of any other words which start with **pre**?

Use a dictionary to help you find them.

Learn, Write, Check.

1. Look carefully at each word.

2. Say the word out loud.

3. Copy each word in your best handwriting.

4. Look again at the first word, then fold the paper over it to cover it.

5. Write the word in COLUMN 3.

6. Check your spelling.

7. Now do the same for each word.

fold line

Name:

Date:

LEARN THE WORD	WRITE THEN COVER	WRITE THEN CHECK
build		
rebuild		
visit		
revisit		
play		
replay		
write		
rewrite		
cycle		
recycle		
place		
replace		
turn		
return		
prepare		
prefix		

● **Changing words by adding er or est.**

fast	slow
faster	slower
fastest	slowest
quick	cold
quicker	colder
quickest	coldest

long

longer	longest

We can change the meaning of some words...

...just by putting a suffix at the end.

Kim's hair is
quite long

Sam's hair is
longer than Kim's
↑
we have added
the suffix **er**

Jasdeep's hair is
longest of all.
↑
we have added
the suffix **est**

Fill in the gaps

long ⟶ longer ⟶ longest

fast ⟶ [   ] ⟶ [   ]

slow ⟶ [   ] ⟶ [   ]

quick ⟶ [   ] ⟶ [   ]

cold ⟶ [   ] ⟶ [   ]

Use fast, faster and fastest to write three sentences.

fold line

Learn, Write, Check.

1. Look carefully at each word.

2. Say the word out loud.

3. Copy each word in your best handwriting.

4. Look again at the first word, then fold the paper over it to cover it.

5. Write the word in COLUMN 3.

6. Check your spelling.

7. Now do the same for each word.

Name:

Date:

LEARN THE WORD	WRITE THEN COVER	WRITE THEN CHECK
fast		
faster		
fastest		
slow		
slower		
slowest		
quick		
quicker		
quickest		
cold		
colder		
coldest		
long		
longer		
longest		

Sheet **A**
For use with OHP, for display or to make matching cards.

● **Changing words which end in e.**

YEAR **3** Term **2**

SET **14** Sheet **A**

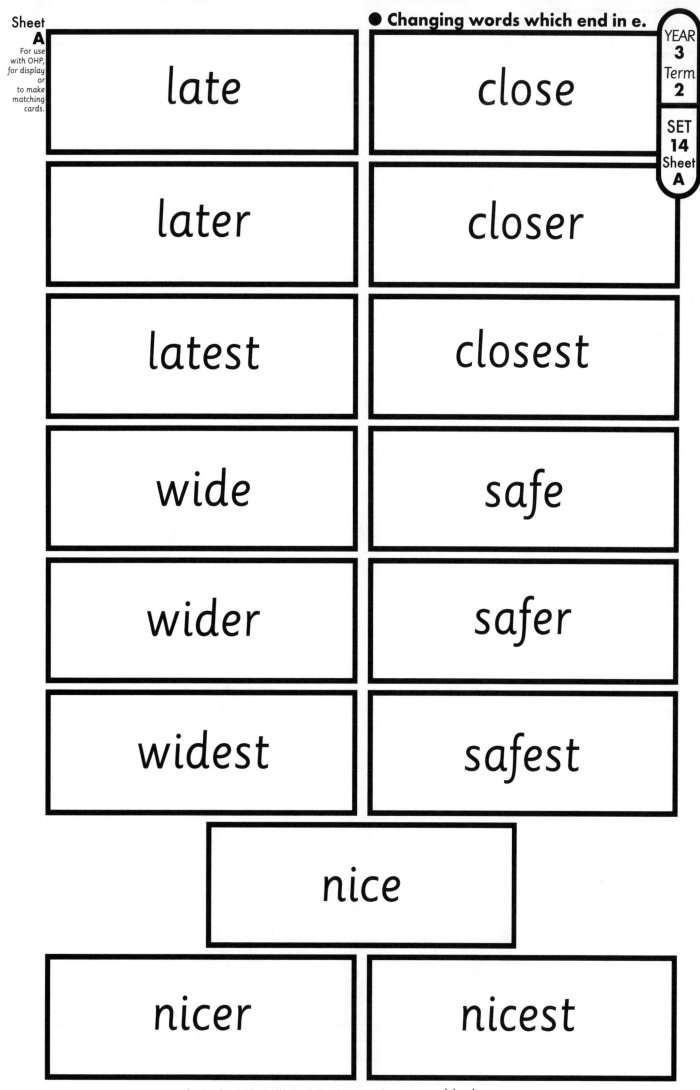

late

close

later

closer

latest

closest

wide

safe

wider

safer

widest

safest

nice

nicer

nicest

If we want to add **er** or **est** to words which end in **e**...

...we have to remove the **e** first.

Look:

   late

   later

   **latest**

remove this e　　　　then add er...　　　　...or est.

Fill in the gaps:

late	⟶	later	⟶	latest
close	⟶		⟶	
wide	⟶		⟶	
safe	⟶		⟶	
nice	⟶		⟶	

Solve the puzzle, using these clues:

Clues across:
1. begins with n and ends with r
2. begins with c and ends with t
3. begins with s and ends with t
4. begins with w and ends with r

Clues down:

5. begins with l and ends with r

6. begins with w and ends with t

7. begins with l and ends with t

8. begins with n and ends with t

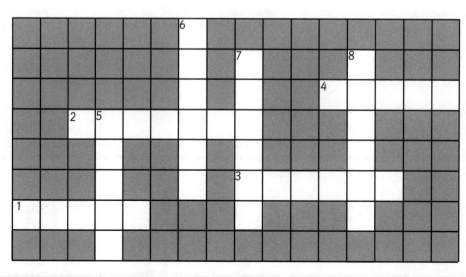

Learn, Write, Check.

1. Look carefully at each word.

2. Say the word out loud.

3. Copy each word in your best handwriting.

4. Look again at the first word, then fold the paper over it to cover it.

5. Write the word in COLUMN 3.

6. Check your spelling.

7. Now do the same for each word.

fold line

Name:

Date:

LEARN THE WORD	WRITE THEN COVER	WRITE THEN CHECK
late		
later		
latest		
close		
closer		
closest		
wide		
wider		
widest		
safe		
safer		
safest		
nice		
nicer		
nicest		

● **Adding er and est to words with short vowels.**

big

fit

bigger

fitter

biggest

fittest

sad

good

sadder

better

saddest

best

bad

worse

worst

Look:

hot   hotter   hottest

short vowel   final consonant   double consonant   double consonant

Try these:

big ⟶ [ ] ⟶ [ ]

fit ⟶ [ ] ⟶ [ ]

sad ⟶ [ ] ⟶ [ ]

Now look at these words which behave very strangely.

good ⟶ better ⟶ best

bad ⟶ worse ⟶ worst

Write three sentences using good, better and best.

fold line

1. Look carefully at each word.

2. Say the word out loud.

3. Copy each word in your best handwriting.

4. Look again at the first word, then fold the paper over it to cover it.

5. Write the word in COLUMN 3.

6. Check your spelling.

7. Now do the same for each word.

Learn, Write, Check.

Name:

Date:

LEARN THE WORD	WRITE THEN COVER	WRITE THEN CHECK
big		
bigger		
biggest		
fit		
fitter		
fittest		
sad		
sadder		
saddest		
good		
better		
best		
bad		
worse		
worst		

Sheet
A
For use
with OHP,
for display
or
to make
matching
cards.

● **Adding er and est to words which end in y.**

happy

foggy

happier

foggier

happiest

foggiest

wavy

funny

wavier

funnier

waviest

funniest

lucky

luckier

luckiest

If a word ends in y...

...we have to change the y to an i to add er or est.

Look:

happy   happier   happiest

↑   ↑   ↑

ends in a y   change the y to an i

Try these:

foggy ⟶ [   ] ⟶ [   ]

wavy ⟶ [   ] ⟶ [   ]

funny ⟶ [   ] ⟶ [   ]

lucky ⟶ [   ] ⟶ [   ]

In your book, write three sentences using funny, funnier and funniest.

Now write three sentences using lucky, luckier and luckiest.

Learn, Write, Check.

fold line

1. Look carefully at each word.

2. Say the word out loud.

3. Copy each word in your best handwriting.

4. Look again at the first word, then fold the paper over it to cover it.

5. Write the word in COLUMN 3.

6. Check your spelling.

7. Now do the same for each word.

Name:

Date:

LEARN THE WORD	WRITE THEN COVER	WRITE THEN CHECK
happy		
happier		
happiest		
foggy		
foggier		
foggiest		
wavy		
wavier		
waviest		
funny		
funnier		
funniest		
lucky		
luckier		
luckiest		

● Changing words by adding y.

Sheet A

For use with OHP, for display or to make matching cards.

mess	messy
ink	inky
full	fully
fuss	fussy
mood	moody
sleep	sleepy
dream	dreamy
cheek	cheeky

Changing words by adding y.

YEAR Term 3 2 | SET Sheet 17 B

If words have two consonants at the end...

...or two vowels before a final consonant...

... it's easy to add y.

Look:

mess → **messy**

two consonants — Just add y

sleep → **sleepy**

two vowels — final consonant — Just add y

Fill the gaps, then add two more words with the same pattern to each column.

mess →	messy		sleep →	sleepy
ink →	☐		mood →	☐
full →	☐		dream →	☐
fuss →	☐		cheek →	☐
☐ →	☐		☐ →	☐
☐ →	☐		☐ →	☐

© Andrew Brodie Publications ✓ www.acblack.com

fold line

1. Look carefully at each word.

2. Say the word out loud.

3. Copy each word in your best handwriting.

4. Look again at the first word, then fold the paper over it to cover it.

5. Write the word in COLUMN 3.

6. Check your spelling.

7. Now do the same for each word.

Learn, Write, Check.

Name:

Date:

LEARN THE WORD	WRITE THEN COVER	WRITE THEN CHECK
mess		
messy		
ink		
inky		
full		
fully		
fuss		
fussy		
mood		
moody		
sleep		
sleepy		
dream		
dreamy		
cheek		
cheeky		

Sheet
A
For use
with OHP,
for display
or
to make
matching
cards.

● Adding y to words with short vowels.

YEAR
3
Term
2

SET
18
Sheet
A

fun	funny
run	runny
sun	sunny
tin	tinny
pop	poppy
dot	dotty
rat	ratty
bat	batty

Is the sun out today?

No, it's not sunny.

Look:

sun ⟶ **sunny**

short vowel   final consonant

two consonants

Fill the gaps.

sun ⟶ sunny   pop ⟶ [ ]

fun ⟶ [ ]   dot ⟶ [ ]

run ⟶ [ ]   rat ⟶ [ ]

tin ⟶ [ ]   bat ⟶ [ ]

Find the correct words to fill these gaps.

He's in a bad mood. He's very [ ] .

A [ ] is a pretty, red flower.

Sam had [ ] at his party.

The jokes were very [ ] .

Now choose four other words to use in sentences.

fold line

1. Look carefully at each word.

2. Say the word out loud.

3. Copy each word in your best handwriting.

4. Look again at the first word, then fold the paper over it to cover it.

5. Write the word in COLUMN 3.

6. Check your spelling.

7. Now do the same for each word.

Learn, Write, Check.

YEAR **3** Term **2**

SET **18** Sheet **C**

Name:

Date:

LEARN THE WORD	WRITE THEN COVER	WRITE THEN CHECK
fun		
funny		
run		
runny		
sun		
sunny		
tin		
tinny		
pop		
poppy		
dot		
dotty		
rat		
ratty		
bat		
batty		

● **Adding y to words ending in e.**

laze	lazy
ease	easy
smoke	smoky
shine	shiny
rose	rosy
stone	stony
breeze	breezy
bone	bony

Adding y to words which end in e.

When words end in e...

...we take off the e to add y.

Look:

smoke ⟶ smoky

Follow the rule to fill these gaps.

smoke ⟶ smoky   rose ⟶ ▢

laze ⟶ ▢   stone ⟶ ▢

ease ⟶ ▢   breeze ⟶ ▢

shine ⟶ ▢   bone ⟶ ▢

Find the correct words to fill these gaps.

We were coughing because the fire was ▢.

Sometimes I just ▢ about doing nothing.

This work is ▢.

My new pound coin is very ▢.

Choose four words from this page. Write a sentence for each one.

© Andrew Brodie Publications ✓ www.acblack.com

1. Look carefully at each word.

2. Say the word out loud.

fold line

3. Copy each word in your best handwriting.

4. Look again at the first word, then fold the paper over it to cover it.

5. Write the word in COLUMN 3.

6. Check your spelling.

7. Now do the same for each word.

Learn, Write, Check.

Name:

Date:

LEARN THE WORD	WRITE THEN COVER	WRITE THEN CHECK
laze		
lazy		
ease		
easy		
smoke		
smoky		
shine		
shiny		
rose		
rosy		
stone		
stony		
breeze		
breezy		
bone		
bony		

Sheet
A
For use
with OHP,
for display
or
to make
matching
cards.

● **Adding s to make plurals.**

boy	boys
girl	girls
table	tables
book	books
desk	desks
time	times
window	windows
house	houses

With some words...

...you just need to add **s** to make them plural.

Look:

one girl ⟶ two girls

Just add s

These words follow the same rule.

table ⟶ [   ]   book ⟶ [   ]

desk ⟶ [   ]   time ⟶ [   ]

window ⟶ [   ]   house ⟶ [   ]

Find some more words which follow this rule.

boy	⟶	boys			⟶	
[ ]	⟶	[ ]		[ ]	⟶	[ ]
[ ]	⟶	[ ]		[ ]	⟶	[ ]

Learn, Write, Check.

fold line

1. Look carefully at each word.

2. Say the word out loud.

3. Copy each word in your best handwriting.

4. Look again at the first word, then fold the paper over it to cover it.

5. Write the word in COLUMN 3.

6. Check your spelling.

7. Now do the same for each word.

Name:

Date:

LEARN THE WORD	WRITE THEN COVER	WRITE THEN CHECK
boy		
boys		
girl		
girls		
table		
tables		
book		
books		
desk		
desks		
time		
times		
window		
windows		
house		
houses		

● **Some words need es to make them plural.**

Sheet
A
For use
with OHP,
for display
or
to make
matching
cards.

catch	catches
match	matches
push	pushes
brush	brushes
blush	blushes
fox	foxes
box	boxes
church	churches

Some words need es to make them plural.

Some words which are singular have one syllable.

When they are made plural they have two syllables.

Look: fox ⟶ foxes

Say this word out loud. It has one syllable.

Say this word out loud. It has two syllables.

Make the singular words plural by adding **es**.

catch ⟶ [ ]   match ⟶ [ ]

push ⟶ [ ]   brush ⟶ [ ]

blush ⟶ [ ]   fox ⟶ [ ]

box ⟶ [ ]   church ⟶ [ ]

Four words in this word bank follow the **es** rule.

WORD BANK

school   book   watch   pocket   ditch   fax

fizz   ruler   pencil

Find the four words and write the singular and plural version of each word.

[ ] ⟶ [ ]   [ ] ⟶ [ ]

[ ] ⟶ [ ]   [ ] ⟶ [ ]

Learn, Write, Check.

1. Look carefully at each word.

2. Say the word out loud.

fold line

3. Copy each word in your best handwriting.

4. Look again at the first word, then fold the paper over it to cover it.

5. Write the word in COLUMN 3.

6. Check your spelling.

7. Now do the same for each word.

Name:

Date:

LEARN THE WORD	WRITE THEN COVER	WRITE THEN CHECK
catch		
catches		
match		
matches		
push		
pushes		
brush		
brushes		
blush		
blushes		
fox		
foxes		
box		
boxes		
church		
churches		

● **Making plurals for words ending in a vowel then y.**

day	days
key	keys
tray	trays
monkey	monkeys
play	plays
holiday	holidays
birthday	birthdays
buy	buys

If a word has a vowel before its final y...

...you just have to add s to make it plural.

day

key

tray

monkey

play

holiday

birthday

buy

Add s to the words on the left.
The first one is done for you.

vowel final y

dáy

↓

days

days

Answer these questions using a sentence for each one:

When is your birthday?

_____

What do you do in the school holidays?

_____

Have you ever seen monkeys in the zoo?

_____

Can you think of any other words which end with a vowel then y?

Learn, Write, Check.

fold line

1. Look carefully at each word.

2. Say the word out loud.

3. Copy each word in your best handwriting.

4. Look again at the first word, then fold the paper over it to cover it.

5. Write the word in COLUMN 3.

6. Check your spelling.

7. Now do the same for each word.

Name:

Date:

LEARN THE WORD	WRITE THEN COVER	WRITE THEN CHECK
day		
days		
key		
keys		
tray		
trays		
monkey		
monkeys		
play		
plays		
holiday		
holidays		
birthday		
birthdays		
buy		
buys		

● **Making plurals for words ending in a consonant then y.**

baby	babies
lady	ladies
puppy	puppies
pony	ponies
party	parties
penny	pennies
hobby	hobbies
fly	flies

If a word has a consonant before its final y...

...you have to replace the y with an i, then add es.

Make the singular words on the left into plural words.
The first one is done for you.

baby   babies

lady

puppy   consonant   final y

pony   pony

party

penny   ponies

hobby   replace the y
with an i...
fly   ...then add es

Find the correct words to fill these gaps.

The dog had six [   ].

Two of my friends had birthdays so I went to both [   ].

There were lots of [   ] by the horse's face.

Fill the gap then answer this question:

How many [   ] make one pound?

fold line

1. Look carefully at each word.

2. Say the word out loud.

3. Copy each word in your best handwriting.

4. Look again at the first word, then fold the paper over it to cover it.

5. Write the word in COLUMN 3.

6. Check your spelling.

7. Now do the same for each word.

Learn, Write, Check.

Name:

Date:

LEARN THE WORD	WRITE THEN COVER	WRITE THEN CHECK
baby		
babies		
lady		
ladies		
puppy		
puppies		
pony		
ponies		
party		
parties		
penny		
pennies		
hobby		
hobbies		
fly		
flies		

Sheet
A
For use
with OHP,
for display
or
to make
matching
cards.

● **Strange plurals.**

YEAR
3
Term
2

SET
24
Sheet
A

man	men
woman	women
child	children
tooth	teeth
mouse	mice
goose	geese
calf	calves
wolf	wolves

The plural of house is houses.

But the plural of mouse is <u>not</u> mouses!

Find the plurals for each of these singular words. Use the words in the word bank.

man ⟶ [   ]

woman ⟶ [   ]

child ⟶ [   ]

tooth ⟶ [   ]

goose ⟶ [   ]

foot ⟶ [   ]

mouse ⟶ [   ]

headlouse ⟶ [   ]

calf ⟶ [   ]

half ⟶ [   ]

wolf ⟶ [   ]

shelf ⟶ [   ]

WORD BANK

children   geese   mice   halves   teeth

women   wolves   headlice   men   feet

calves   shelves

Write a sentence to answer this question:

How many teeth have you got?

_____

Now choose four more words from this page. Write a question sentence for each one.

Learn, Write, Check.

1. Look carefully at each word.

2. Say the word out loud.

3. Copy each word in your best handwriting.

4. Look again at the first word, then fold the paper over it to cover it.

5. Write the word in COLUMN 3.

6. Check your spelling.

7. Now do the same for each word.

fold line

Name:

Date:

LEARN THE WORD	WRITE THEN COVER	WRITE THEN CHECK
man		
men		
woman		
women		
child		
children		
tooth		
teeth		
mouse		
mice		
goose		
geese		
calf		
calves		
wolf		
wolves		

Sheet
A
For use
with OHP,
for display
or
to make
matching
cards.

knee	kneel
knife	knives
know	knock
gnat	gnome
write	wrist
wrap	wrapping
when	where
honest	rhyme

Some words include letters which make no sound at all.

We call these silent letters.

WORD BANK

rhyme   knives   kneel   gnome   wrap   knee
honest   where   knock   wrapping   knife
write   gnat   know   wrist   when

In the word bank: four words have silent h
four words have silent w
two words have silent g
six words have silent k.

Write the words in the correct list below. See if you can think of an extra word for each list.

silent h	silent w	silent g	silent k

fold line

1. Look carefully at each word.

2. Say the word out loud.

3. Copy each word in your best handwriting.

4. Look again at the first word, then fold the paper over it to cover it.

5. Write the word in COLUMN 3.

6. Check your spelling.

7. Now do the same for each word.

Learn, Write, Check.

Name:

Date:

LEARN THE WORD	WRITE THEN COVER	WRITE THEN CHECK
knee		
kneel		
knife		
knives		
know		
knock		
gnat		
gnome		
write		
wrist		
wrap		
wrapping		
when		
where		
honest		
rhyme		

Sheet
A
For use
with OHP,
for display
or
to make
matching
cards.

● **More silent letters.**

comb	bomb
thumb	crumb
lamb	numb
calf	calves
half	halves
calm	palm

could

should	would

On this page, six words have silent b...

...and nine words have silent l.

WORD BANK

halves   could   crumb   palm   should   bomb

half   calm   calf   comb   thumb

calves   would   lamb   numb

Sort the words in the word bank into two sets.

silent b words

silent l words

Write a sentence which includes the words:

lamb   calf

_____

_____

Now try writing a sentence which includes five words with silent letters. This could be tricky!

_____

_____

fold line

1. Look carefully at each word.

2. Say the word out loud.

3. Copy each word in your best handwriting.

4. Look again at the first word, then fold the paper over it to cover it.

5. Write the word in COLUMN 3.

6. Check your spelling.

7. Now do the same for each word.

Learn, Write, Check.

Name:

Date:

LEARN THE WORD	WRITE THEN COVER	WRITE THEN CHECK
comb		
bomb		
thumb		
crumb		
lamb		
numb		
calf		
calves		
half		
halves		
calm		
palm		
could		
should		
would		

Sheet
A
For use
with OHP,
for display
or
to make
matching
cards.

play	playground
motor	motorway
bed	bedroom
every	everybody
everyone	everything
some	somebody
someone	something
somewhere	sometimes

We have started this chart for you. Can you finish it by filling in the gaps?

every	⟶	body	⟶	everybody
bed	⟶	room	⟶	
every	⟶		⟶	everything
some	⟶	where	⟶	
some	⟶		⟶	somebody
some	⟶	thing	⟶	
every	⟶	one	⟶	
play	⟶	ground	⟶	
some	⟶		⟶	someone
some	⟶	times	⟶	
motor	⟶	way	⟶	

Words which are made by joining others together are called **compound** words.
Can you think of four other compound words?

Learn, Write, Check.

1. Look carefully at each word.

2. Say the word out loud.

3. Copy each word in your best handwriting.

4. Look again at the first word, then fold the paper over it to cover it.

5. Write the word in COLUMN 3.

6. Check your spelling.

7. Now do the same for each word.

fold line

Name:

Date:

LEARN THE WORD	WRITE THEN COVER	WRITE THEN CHECK
play		
playground		
motor		
motorway		
bed		
bedroom		
every		
everybody		
everyone		
everything		
some		
somebody		
someone		
something		
somewhere		
sometimes		

Sheet
A
For use
with OHP,
for display
or
to make
matching
cards.

● **More compound words.**

pan	pancake
week	weekend
goal	goalkeeper
break	breakfast
stairs	upstairs
downstairs	any
anybody	anyone
anything	anywhere

How many words can you think of which end with **body** ?

I can think of: **anybody, nobody, somebody** and **everybody.**

START WORDS
pan   down   up   any
goal   week   break
some

END WORDS
one   stairs   fast   cake
thing   keeper   body
where   end   times

Make some compound words using the START WORDS and END WORDS above.
Some of them can be used more than once.

START WORD		END WORD		COMPOUND WORD
	→		→	
	→		→	
	→		→	
	→		→	
	→		→	
	→		→	
	→		→	
	→		→	

fold line

3. Copy each word in your best handwriting.

4. Look again at the first word, then fold the paper over it to cover it.

5. Write the word in COLUMN 3.

6. Check your spelling.

7. Now do the same for each word.

Learn, Write, Check.

Name:

Date:

1. Look carefully at each word.

2. Say the word out loud.

LEARN THE WORD	WRITE THEN COVER	WRITE THEN CHECK
pan		
pancake		
week		
weekend		
goal		
goalkeeper		
break		
breakfast		
stairs		
upstairs		
downstairs		
any		
anybody		
anyone		
anything		
anywhere		

YEAR
3
Term
2

SET
29
Sheet
A

Sheet
A
For use
with OHP,
for display
or
to make
matching
cards.

love	lovely
nice	nicely
like	likely
safe	safely
real	really
usual	usually
regular	regularly
proper	properly

Suffixes.

Suffixes are extra parts added to the ends of some words.

For example, we can add ly to the word **love** and make **lovely**.

Add ly to these words to make new words.

love ⟶ [ ] nice ⟶ [ ]

like ⟶ [ ] safe ⟶ [ ]

real ⟶ [ ] usual ⟶ [ ]

regular ⟶ [ ] proper ⟶ [ ]

Check that your words look exactly like these:

lovely   nicely   likely   safely   really

usually   regularly   properly

Choose one of these words to fill the gap in each of these sentences.

Rain in January is quite [ ] .

Swimming is [ ] good fun.

You must cross the road [ ] .

Now write three sentences of your own. Use a word which ends in ly in each sentence.

1. Look carefully at each word.

2. Say the word out loud.

3. Copy each word in your best handwriting.

4. Look again at the first word, then fold the paper over it to cover it.

5. Write the word in COLUMN 3.

6. Check your spelling.

7. Now do the same for each word.

fold line

Learn, Write, Check.

Name:

Date:

LEARN THE WORD	WRITE THEN COVER	WRITE THEN CHECK
love		
lovely		
nice		
nicely		
like		
likely		
safe		
safely		
real		
really		
usual		
usually		
regular		
regularly		
proper		
properly		

Sheet
A
For use
with OHP,
for display
or
to make
matching
cards.

● **Suffixes: adding ful.**

YEAR
3
Term
2

SET
30
Sheet
A

hope	hopeful
care	careful
pain	painful
use	useful
wonder	wonderful
cheer	cheerful
beauty	beautiful
till	until

Some words can have the suffix ful added to them.

Careful means full of care.

full of care ➡ careful

double l

single l

Add the suffix ful to these words.

hope	⟶		pain	⟶
use	⟶		wonder	⟶
cheer	⟶		care	⟶

Look carefully at this one:

beauty ➡ beautiful

letter y

we have replaced the y with an i

Practise writing beauty and beautiful.

A different ending:

Read these two sentences:

I stayed out till late.

I stayed out until 10 o'clock.

till ➡ until

double l

single l

Write two sentences including the words till and until.

fold line

1. Look carefully at each word.

2. Say the word out loud.

3. Copy each word in your best handwriting.

4. Look again at the first word, then fold the paper over it to cover it.

5. Write the word in COLUMN 3.

6. Check your spelling.

7. Now do the same for each word.

Learn, Write, Check.

YEAR **3** Term **2**

SET **30** Sheet **C**

Name:

Date:

LEARN THE WORD	WRITE THEN COVER	WRITE THEN CHECK
hope		
hopeful		
care		
careful		
pain		
painful		
use		
useful		
wonder		
wonderful		
cheer		
cheerful		
beauty		
beautiful		
till		
until		

● **Suffixes: adding less.**

YEAR
3
Term
2

SET
31
Sheet
A

Sheet
A
For use
with OHP,
for display
or
to make
matching
cards.

hope	hopeless
care	careless
pain	painless
use	useless
home	homeless
speech	speechless
end	endless
harm	harmless

Some words can have the suffix less added to them.

Harmless means there is no harm.

Add the suffix less to these words.

hope ⟶ [ ]   care ⟶ [ ]

pain ⟶ [ ]   use ⟶ [ ]

home ⟶ [ ]   speech ⟶ [ ]

end ⟶ [ ]   harm ⟶ [ ]

Fill in the missing words.

Some snakes can bite but some are [ ] .

Usually, having an injection is [ ] .

Sometimes I make [ ] mistakes.

Try to complete this crossword:

CLUES ACROSS
1. Not speaking at all.
3. No hope.
4. Without end.
5. No pain.

CLUES DOWN
2. Not careful
3. Not dangerous.

Learn, Write, Check.

fold line

1. Look carefully at each word.

2. Say the word out loud.

3. Copy each word in your best handwriting.

4. Look again at the first word, then fold the paper over it to cover it.

5. Write the word in COLUMN 3.

6. Check your spelling.

7. Now do the same for each word.

Name:

Date:

LEARN THE WORD	WRITE THEN COVER	WRITE THEN CHECK
hope		
hopeless		
care		
careless		
pain		
painless		
use		
useless		
home		
homeless		
speech		
speechless		
end		
endless		
harm		
harmless		

Sheet
A
For use
with OHP,
for display
or
to make
matching
cards.

● **Suffixes: adding er.**

YEAR
3
Term
2

SET
32
Sheet
A

teach	teacher
farm	farmer
drive	driver
mine	miner
babysit	babysitter
run	runner
shop	shopper
spin	spinner

Sometimes we have to change the end of a word when we want to add er.

Look carefully at the words on this page.

For these words we <u>just add er</u>:

teach ⟶ [   ]   farm ⟶ [   ]

For these words we <u>take off e, then add er</u>:

mine ⟶ [   ]   drive ⟶ [   ]

For these words we <u>double the end consonant, then add er</u>:

babysit ⟶ [   ]   run ⟶ [   ]

shop ⟶ [   ]   spin ⟶ [   ]

Check that your words look exactly like these:

teacher   farmer   miner   driver   babysitter
runner   shopper   spinner

Find the correct word to match each clue:

Operates a car ⟶ [   ]

Milks the cows ⟶ [   ]

Works at school ⟶ [   ]

Looks after children when their mum and dad are out ⟶ [   ]

Runs in race ⟶ [   ]

Learn, Write, Check.

fold line

1. Look carefully at each word.

2. Say the word out loud.

3. Copy each word in your best handwriting.

4. Look again at the first word, then fold the paper over it to cover it.

5. Write the word in COLUMN 3.

6. Check your spelling.

7. Now do the same for each word.

Name:

Date:

LEARN THE WORD	WRITE THEN COVER	WRITE THEN CHECK
teach		
teacher		
farm		
farmer		
drive		
driver		
mine		
miner		
babysit		
babysitter		
run		
runner		
shop		
shopper		
spin		
spinner		

● **Using apostrophes.**

Sheet
A
For use
with OHP,
for display
or
to make
matching
cards.

is not	isn't
was not	wasn't
did not	didn't
does not	doesn't
will not	won't
cannot	can't
could not	couldn't
should not	shouldn't

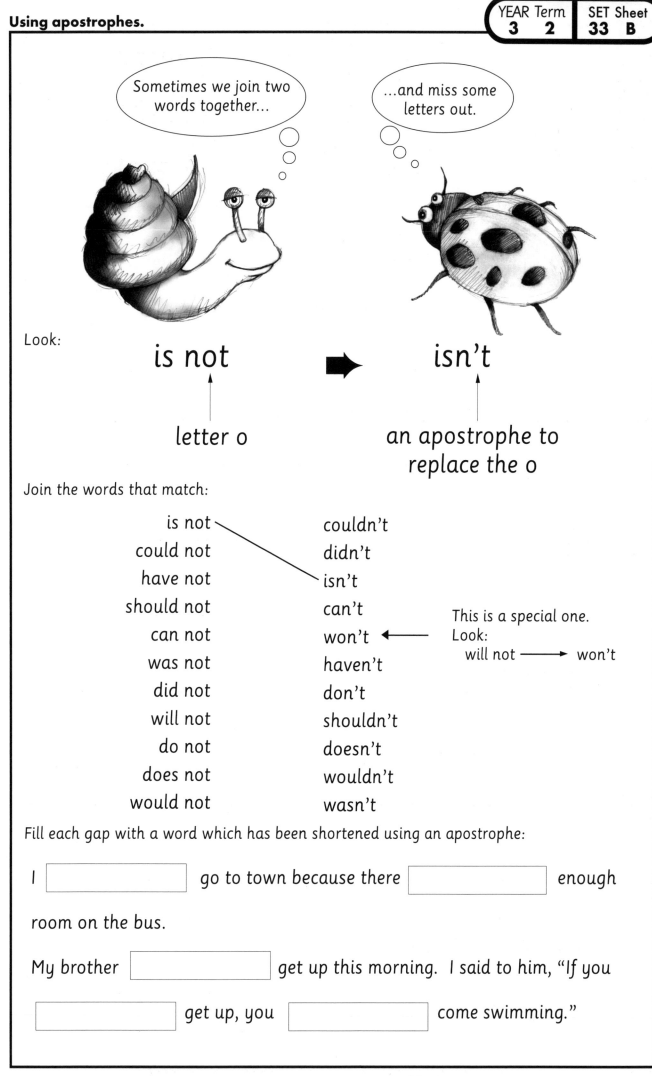

Sometimes we join two words together...

...and miss some letters out.

Look:

is not ➡ isn't

letter o

an apostrophe to replace the o

Join the words that match:

is not   couldn't
could not   didn't
have not   isn't
should not   can't
can not   won't ← This is a special one.
was not   haven't   Look:
did not   don't   will not ⟶ won't
will not   shouldn't
do not   doesn't
does not   wouldn't
would not   wasn't

Fill each gap with a word which has been shortened using an apostrophe:

I [   ] go to town because there [   ] enough

room on the bus.

My brother [   ] get up this morning. I said to him, "If you

[   ] get up, you [   ] come swimming."

Learn, Write, Check.

fold line

1. Look carefully at each word.

2. Say the word out loud.

3. Copy each word in your best handwriting.

4. Look again at the first word, then fold the paper over it to cover it.

5. Write the word in COLUMN 3.

6. Check your spelling.

7. Now do the same for each word.

Name:

Date:

LEARN THE WORD	WRITE THEN COVER	WRITE THEN CHECK
is not		
isn't		
was not		
wasn't		
did not		
didn't		
does not		
doesn't		
will not		
won't		
cannot		
can't		
could not		
couldn't		
should not		
shouldn't		

Sheet
A
For use
with OHP,
for display
or
to make
matching
cards.

● **More apostrophes.**

I would	I'd
I have	I've
they have	they've
she will	she'll
there is	there's
where is	where's
here is	here's
they are	they're

Where's my shell?

It's on your back.

Look:

where's ➡ where is   it's ➡ it is

Join the words that match in these sets.
We've done some of them for you.

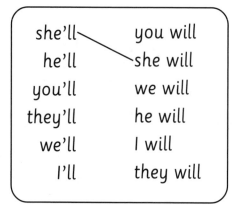

she'll	you will
he'll	she will
you'll	we will
they'll	he will
we'll	I will
I'll	they will

where's	he is
there's	here is
here's	she is
it's	where is
he's	it is
she's	there is

we've	they have
I've	you have
they've	we have
you've	I have

we'd	I would
you'd	we would
I'd	you would

Notice that some words
appear in both of these boxes
but mean different things.

she'd	you had
you'd	I had
I'd	she had

Fill the gaps in this conversation:

" [   ] the dog?" asked Mum.

" [   ] over there," I said.

" [   ] better go and get him," Mum said.

Now write a short conversation of your own.

fold line

1. Look carefully at each word.

2. Say the word out loud.

3. Copy each word in your best handwriting.

4. Look again at the first word, then fold the paper over it to cover it.

5. Write the word in COLUMN 3.

6. Check your spelling.

7. Now do the same for each word.

Learn, Write, Check.

Name:

Date:

LEARN THE WORD	WRITE THEN COVER	WRITE THEN CHECK
I would		
I'd		
I have		
I've		
they have		
they've		
she will		
she'll		
there is		
there's		
where is		
where's		
here is		
here's		
they are		
they're		

Sheet
A
For use
with OHP,
for display
or
to make
matching
cards.

behave	misbehave
sense	nonsense
fiction	non-fiction
stop	non-stop
import	export
interior	exterior
star	co-star
clockwise	anticlockwise

Prefixes are extra parts added to the start of some words.

They change the meaning of the words.

Practise the word pairs:

behave	misbehave

sense	nonsense

fiction	non-fiction

stop	non-stop

import	export

interior	exterior

star	co-star

clockwise	anticlockwise

Some of the words above give the answers to this crossword.

CLUES DOWN

2.   Not making sense.
7.   Outside a building.
8.   Don't go.

CLUES ACROSS

1.   The direction of a clock's hands.
3.   When you are good, you _____ .
4.   Inside a building.
5.   Story books.
6.   A famous person or something that twinkles in the night sky.

1. Look carefully at each word.

2. Say the word out loud.

fold line

3. Copy each word in your best handwriting.

4. Look again at the first word, then fold the paper over it to cover it.

5. Write the word in COLUMN 3.

6. Check your spelling.

7. Now do the same for each word.

Learn, Write, Check.

Name:

Date:

LEARN THE WORD	WRITE THEN COVER	WRITE THEN CHECK
behave		
misbehave		
sense		
nonsense		
fiction		
non-fiction		
stop		
non-stop		
import		
export		
interior		
exterior		
star		
co-star		
clockwise		
anticlockwise		

Sheet
A
For use
with OHP,
for display
or
to make
matching
cards.

● **Prefixes.**

YEAR
3
Term
3

SET
36
Sheet
A

cycle	bicycle
recycle	tricycle
appear	disappear
visible	invisible
normal	abnormal
view	preview
review	interview
marine	submarine

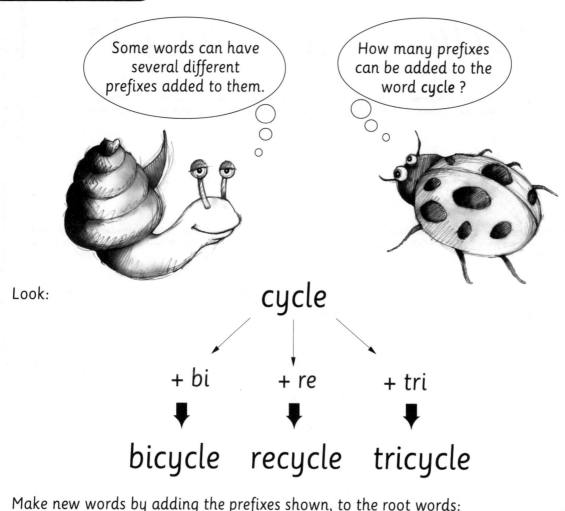

Some words can have several different prefixes added to them.

How many prefixes can be added to the word **cycle** ?

Look:

cycle

+ bi   + re   + tri

bicycle   **recycle**   **tricycle**

Make new words by adding the prefixes shown, to the root words:

cycle	+ bi	➡	
cycle	+ re	➡	
cycle	+ tri	➡	
appear	+ dis	➡	
visible	+ in	➡	
normal	+ ab	➡	
view	+ pre	➡	
view	+ re	➡	
view	+ inter	➡	
marine	+ sub	➡	

Can you think of some other words which start with **inter**?

Learn, Write, Check.

1. Look carefully at each word.

2. Say the word out loud.

fold line

3. Copy each word in your best handwriting.

4. Look again at the first word, then fold the paper over it to cover it.

5. Write the word in COLUMN 3.

6. Check your spelling.

7. Now do the same for each word.

Name:

Date:

LEARN THE WORD	WRITE THEN COVER	WRITE THEN CHECK
cycle		
bicycle		
recycle		
tricycle		
appear		
disappear		
visible		
invisible		
normal		
abnormal		
view		
preview		
review		
interview		
marine		
submarine		

● Days.

Sheet
A
For use
with OHP,
for display
or
to make
matching
cards.

Monday	Tuesday
Wednesday	Thursday
Friday	Saturday
Sunday	holiday
yesterday	tomorrow
birthday	anniversary
weekday	weekend
fortnight	tonight

Write the days of the week in the right order.

Try to make no mistakes with the spellings.

JUMBLED DAYS

Wednesday   Saturday   Monday   Friday
Sunday   Thursday   Tuesday

1 _____ 2 _____ 3 _____

4 _____ 5 _____ 6 _____ 7 _____

Here are some more words to do with days:

holiday   yesterday   tomorrow   birthday   anniversary   week
weekday   weekend   fortnight   tonight   today

Solve this puzzle using some of the words.

CLUES ACROSS

2. I like the summer _____ .
3. The day after today.
4. I might have a party for my _____ .
6. The two days which are not school days.
7. This day itself.

CLUES DOWN

1. Two weeks make a _____ .
5. The day before today.
7. I will go to bed _____ .

fold line

1. Look carefully at each word.

2. Say the word out loud.

3. Copy each word in your best handwriting.

4. Look again at the first word, then fold the paper over it to cover it.

5. Write the word in COLUMN 3.

6. Check your spelling.

7. Now do the same for each word.

Learn, Write, Check.

Name:

Date:

LEARN THE WORD	WRITE THEN COVER	WRITE THEN CHECK
Monday		
Tuesday		
Wednesday		
Thursday		
Friday		
Saturday		
Sunday		
holiday		
yesterday		
tomorrow		
birthday		
anniversary		
weekday		
weekend		
fortnight		
tonight		

Sheet
A
For use
with OHP,
for display
or
to make
matching
cards.

● **Months and seasons.**

YEAR
3
Term
3

SET
38
Sheet
A

January	February
March	April
May	June
July	August
September	October
November	December
spring	summer
autumn	fwinter

Some months have thirty days and some have thirty-one days.

February is strange. It has twenty-eight days and twenty-nine days in a leap year.

Copy out this rhyme in your best handwriting.

Thirty days has September,
April, June and November.
All the rest have thirty-one,
    except for February alone,
Which has twenty-eight days clear
and twenty-nine in each leap year.

_____

_____

_____

_____

_____

_____

_____

_____

Which month usually has 28 days? [   ]

Which months have 30 days?

[   ] [   ] [   ] [   ]

Which months have 31 days?

[   ] [   ] [   ] [   ]

[   ] [   ] [   ]

1. Look carefully at each word.

2. Say the word out loud.

3. Copy each word in your best handwriting.

4. Look again at the first word, then fold the paper over it to cover it.

5. Write the word in COLUMN 3.

6. Check your spelling.

7. Now do the same for each word.

Learn, Write, Check.

YEAR **3**
Term **3**

SET **38**
Sheet **C**

Name:

Date:

LEARN THE WORD	WRITE THEN COVER	WRITE THEN CHECK
January		
February		
March		
April		
May		
June		
July		
August		
September		
October		
November		
December		
spring		
summer		
autumn		
winter		

● **Numbers.**

YEAR
3
Term
3

SET
39
Sheet
A

Sheet
A
For use
with OHP,
for display
or
to make
matching
cards.

eleven	twelve
thirteen	fourteen
fifteen	sixteen
seventeen	eighteen
nineteen	twenty
thirty	forty
fifty	sixty
seventy	eighty

We sometimes write numbers using numerals...

...and sometimes we use words.

NUMBER WORD BANK

eleven   twelve   thirteen   fourteen   fifteen

sixteen   seventeen   eighteen   nineteen   twenty

thirty   forty   fifty   sixty   seventy   eighty

Write the correct words to match the numbers written in numerals.

NUMERALS	WORDS	NUMERALS	WORDS
20	twenty	13	
17		80	
11		12	
60		70	
16		14	
19		40	
50		18	
30		15	

Look, these words have a letter u: four   fourteen

This word does not have a letter u: forty

Learn, Write, Check.

1. Look carefully at each word.

2. Say the word out loud.

fold line

3. Copy each word in your best handwriting.

4. Look again at the first word, then fold the paper over it to cover it.

5. Write the word in COLUMN 3.

6. Check your spelling.

7. Now do the same for each word.

Name:

Date:

LEARN THE WORD	WRITE THEN COVER	WRITE THEN CHECK
eleven		
twelve		
thirteen		
fourteen		
fifteen		
sixteen		
seventeen		
eighteen		
nineteen		
twenty		
thirty		
forty		
fifty		
sixty		
seventy		
eighty		

Sheet
A

For use
with OHP,
for display
or
to make
matching
cards.

● **Numbers and measurements.**

YEAR
3
Term
3

SET
40
Sheet
A

ninety	hundred
thousand	million
metre	centimetre
millimetre	kilometre
gram	kilogram
litre	millilitre
second	minute
hour	month

On this page we have some big numbers...

...and some words to do with measuring.

Match the numerals to the number words.

90	thousand
100	ninety
1000	million
1000000	hundred

Copy the words.

Label the hands on the clock, using these words: second   minute   hour

_____ hand.

_____ hand.

_____ hand.

Write the correct measurement word for each abbreviation:

MEASUREMENT WORDS

metre   centimetre   millimetre   kilometre

gram   kilogram   litre   millilitre

cm ⟶

m ⟶

ml ⟶

mm ⟶

km ⟶

l ⟶

kg ⟶

g ⟶

fold line

Learn, Write, Check.

YEAR
3
Term
3

SET
40
Sheet
C

1. Look carefully at each word.

2. Say the word out loud.

3. Copy each word in your best handwriting.

4. Look again at the first word, then fold the paper over it to cover it.

5. Write the word in COLUMN 3.

6. Check your spelling.

7. Now do the same for each word.

Name:

Date:

LEARN THE WORD	WRITE THEN COVER	WRITE THEN CHECK
ninety		
hundred		
thousand		
million		
metre		
centimetre		
millimetre		
kilometre		
gram		
kilogram		
litre		
millilitre		
second		
minute		
hour		
month		

Some of the activities on Sheet B for each set of words require answers which are individual to the pupils. Some, however, have standard answers and we list these below to save time for teachers in marking pupils' work.

Set 1, Sheet B   ringing, walking, jumping, painting, dressing, resting, calling
Missing words: dressing, jumping, calling, painting, ringing, singing

Set 2, Sheet B   dreaming, feeling, shouting, sailing, boiling, peeling, speaking
Missing words: sweeping, sailing, nailing, eating, treating, looking, cooking

Set 3, Sheet B   hopping, sitting, skipping, stepping, gripping, shutting, winning
Missing words: skipping, skipping, gripping, shutting, running
humming, winning, spinning, swimming, stopping

Set 4, Sheet B   coming, smiling, taking, caring, making, dividing, staring
Root words: shine, tune, rhyme, time

Set 5, Sheet B   double z: dazzle, nuzzle, puzzle   double b: wobble, dribble, nibble
double d: middle, muddle, saddle, fiddle, puddle, paddle
double g: giggle, wiggle   double t: little, nettle, kettle, rattle, cattle

Set 6, Sheet B   trickling, pickling, prickling, crackling, tackling, chuckling, buckling
Missing words: pickle, trickling, chuckling

Set 7, Sheet B   able words: able, table, valuable, cable, vegetable, portable, reliable, probable
ible words: horrible, sensible, terrible, possible, invisible, impossible, visible, responsible
Extension activity: lovable, forgivable, believable, movable, removable

Set 8, Sheet B   Cannot end in ing: thimble, fable, simple, example
Letter u followed by letter m: crumple, bumble, jumble, mumble, tumble, grumble, stumble
Letter o followed by letter u: double, trouble
Letter m but no letter u: thimble, scramble, simple, example, sample
Words ending in ple: crumple, simple, example, sample

Set 9, Sheet B   …cle words: miracle, cycle, uncle, circle, bicycle, icicle
…dle words: candle, trundle, handle, bundle, needle
…gle words: bungle, jungle, single, jingle, tingle

Set 10, Sheet B   untidy, unlucky, unusual, unzip, untie, unfair, unkind
Missing words: unhappy, unzip, untie, unkind (or unfair)

Set 11, Sheet B   disagree, disappear, disconnect, dishonest, disobey

Set 12, Sheet B   revisit, replay, rewrite, recycle, replace, return

Set 13, Sheet B   faster, fastest   slower, slowest   quicker, quickest   colder, coldest

Set 14, Sheet B closer, closest   wider, widest   safer, safest   nicer, nicest

						^{6}w								
						i		^{7}l				^{8}n		
						d		a			^{4}w	i	d	e	r
		^{2}c	^{5}l	o	s	e	s	t				c		
			a			s		e				e		
			t			t		^{3}s	a	f	e	s	t
^{1}n	i	c	e	r				t				t	
			r										

Set 15, Sheet B bigger, biggest   fitter, fittest   sadder, saddest
Set 16, Sheet B foggier, foggiest   wavier, waviest   funnier, funniest   luckier, luckiest
Set 17, Sheet B inky, fully, fussy,   moody, dreamy, cheeky
Set 18, Sheet B funny, runny, tinny, poppy, dotty, ratty, batty
Missing words: ratty, poppy, fun, funny
Set 19, Sheet B lazy, easy, shiny, rosy, stony, breezy, bony
Missing words: smoky, laze, easy, shiny
Set 20, Sheet B tables, desks, windows, books, times, houses
Set 21, Sheet B catches, pushes, blushes, boxes, matches, brushes, foxes, churches
watch: watches   ditch: ditches   fax: faxes   fizz: fizzes
Set 22, Sheet B keys, trays, monkeys, plays, holidays, birthdays, buys
Set 23, Sheet B ladies, puppies, ponies, parties, pennies, hobbies, flies
Missing words: puppies, parties, flies, pennies
Set 24, Sheet B men, women, children   teeth, geese, feet   mice, headlice
calves, halves, wolves, shelves
Set 25, Sheet B silent h: rhyme, honest, where, when   silent w: wrap, wrapping, write, wrist
silent g: gnome, gnat   silent k: knives, kneel, knee, knock, knife, know
Set 26, Sheet B silent b: crumb, bomb, comb, thumb, lamb, numb
silent l: halves, could, palm, should, half, calm, calf, calves, would
Set 27, Sheet B bedroom, thing, somewhere, body, something, everyone, playground
one, sometimes, motorway
Set 28, Sheet B Pupils can choose any eight compound words from those listed here:
pan, cake: pancake   down, stairs: downstairs   up, stairs: upstairs
(up, end: up-end)   any, one: anyone   any, thing: anything
any, body: anybody   any, where: anywhere   goal, keeper: goalkeeper
week, end: weekend   break, fast: breakfast   some, one: someone
some, thing: something   some, body: somebody   some, where: somewhere
some, times: sometimes
Set 29, Sheet B lovely, likely, really, regularly, nicely, safely, usually, properly
Missing words: likely, really, safely
Set 30, Sheet B hopeful, useful, cheerful, painful, wonderful, careful
Set 31, Sheet B hopeless, painless, homeless, endless, careless, useless, speechless, harmless
Missing words: harmless, painless, careless
Crossword: Across: 1. speechless 3. hopeless 4. endless 5. painless
Down: 2. careless 3. harmless
Set 32, Sheet B teacher, farmer
miner, driver
babysitter, shopper, runner, spinner
Missing words: driver, farmer, teacher, babysitter, runner

ANSWERS

Set 33, Sheet B

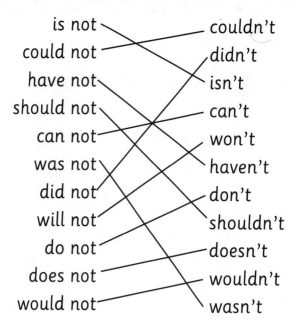

Missing words:
couldn't, wasn't

wouldn't, don't, can't

Set 34, Sheet B

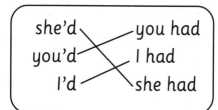

Missing words: Where's, He's, You'd

Set 35, Sheet B   Answers across: 1. clockwise   3. behave   4. interior   5. fiction   6. star
Answers down: 2. nonsense   7. exterior   8. stop

Set 36, Sheet B   bicycle, recycle, tricycle, disappear, invisible, abnormal, preview, review
interview, submarine

Set 37, Sheet B   1. Monday   2. Tuesday   3. Wednesday   4. Thursday   5. Friday
6. Saturday   7. Sunday
Answers across: 2. holiday   3. tomorrow   4. birthday   6. weekend   7. today
Answers down: 1. fortnight   5. yesterday   7. tonight

Set 38, Sheet B   February   April, June, September, November
January, March, May, July, August, October, December

Set 39, Sheet B   1st column: seventeen, eleven, sixty, sixteen, nineteen, fifty, thirty
2nd column: thirteen, eighty, twelve, seventy, fourteen, forty, eighteen, fifteen

Set 40, Sheet B   Clock hands: minute, hour, second